ASIAPAC COMIC

THE 8 IMMORTALS

The Eight Immortals Cross The Sea

八仙过海

● Illustrated by **Chan Kok Sing** ● Translated by **Koh Kok Kiang**

⏛ ASIAPAC • SINGAPORE

isher
ASIAPAC BOOKS PTE LTD
996 Bendemeer Road #06-08/09   Singapore 339944
Tel: (65) 6392 8455   Fax: (65) 6392 6455
Email asiapacbooks@pacific.net.sg

Visit us at our Internet home page
www.asiapacbooks.com

First published February 2001
8th edition May 2007

© 1999 ASIAPAC BOOKS, SINGAPORE
ISBN 981-229-084-2

Bibliographic Data
```
LDR         nam a     00
001         ASP1013
005         20011009102723.0
008         010929s1999    si     a       000 0 eng d
020         ǂa9812290842 (pbk.)
041   1     ǂaengǂhchi
050   14    ǂaBL1923ǂb.C43 1999
082   0     ǂa299.514213ǂ221
100   1     ǂaChan, Kok Sing.
245   14    ǂaThe 8 immortals :ǂbthe eight immortals cross the sea /
            ǂcillustrated by Chan Kok Sing ; translated by Koh Kok
            Kiang.
260         ǂaSingapore :ǂbAsiapac,ǂc1999.
300         ǂa122 p. :ǂbchiefly ill. ;ǂc21 cm.
440   0     ǂaAsiapac comic series
650   0     ǂaBa Xian (Taoist mythology)ǂvCaricatures and cartoons.
650   0     ǂaMythology, TaoistǂvCaricatures and cartoons.
650   0     ǂaGods, TaoistǂvCaricatures and cartoons.
700   1     ǂaKoh, Kok Kiang.
```

Cover illustration by Chan Kok Sing
Cover design by ILLUSION Creative Studio
Body text in 8/9 pt Helvetica
Printed in Singapore by Loi Printing

Publisher's Note

As a publisher dedicated to the promotion of works of Chinese philosophy, art and literature, we are pleased to bring you this graphic presentation of *The Eight Immortals: The Eight Immortals Cross The Sea*.

The Eight Immortals are among the most popular figures of Chinese myths and legends. In fact they are the legendary figures closest to the hearts of the ordinary people. The stories in this book show how eight ordinary people in ancient China attain immortality through selfless actions and good deeds. The climax is, of course, how the Eight Immortals cross the Eastern Sea after attending the Peach of Immortality Gathering hosted by the Queen Mother. You will be enthralled by the vivid description of the great battle at the palace of the Dragon King.

We would like to take this opportunity to thank Chan Kok Sing for his lively comic illustrations. Our appreciation, too, to Koh Kok Kiang for translating this volume and writing the Introduction, and the production team for putting in their best effort in the publication of this book.

Asiapac Comics Series by Chan Kok Sing

Ji Gong the Crazy Monk
Ji Gong Saves the Day
The Eight Immortals: The Eight Immortals Cross the Sea
The Eight Immortals: Uproar in the Celestial Palace
The Eight Immortals: Rewarding the Honest
The Eight Immortals: Miracle workers
Patron Gods of Popular Chinese Trades
Zhong Kui the Ghostcatcher
Zhong Kui Tames a Vengeful Soul
Nuggets of Wisdom from Aesop's Fables

About the Illustrator

Chan Kok Sing 陈国胜 is a Malaysian artist born in 1971. A lover of nature and the simple life, he enjoys physical exercise and reading. Upon completion of his secondary education in 1990, he took up a course in pure art at the College of Art, Kuala Lumpur, and graduated in 1995. Since then, he has published many of his comics and illustrations in various newspapers in Malaysia.

He has also illustrated other titles in Asiapac Comic Series, namely *The Eight Immortals: Eight Immortals Cross the Sea*; *The Eight Immortals: Uproar in the Celestial Palace*; *The Eight Immortals: Rewarding the Honest*; *The Eight Immortals: Miracle Workers*; *Zhong Kui the Ghostcatcher*; *Zhong Kui Tames A Vengeful Soul*; *Patron Gods of Popular Chinese Trades*; *Ji Gong the Crazy Monk;* and *Ji Gong Saves the Day*. He was duly rewarded with The Culture Award during the 1999 Asia Manga Summit in Taipei for his contributions to culture. His aspiration is to have an art studio of his own.

Introduction

Among the popular figures of Chinese myths and legends, the Eight Immortals of Taoist folk religion stand out.

They are probably the ones closest to the hearts of the ordinary Chinese as they represent all conditions of life—poverty, wealth, nobility, plebeianism, age, youth, masculinity and femininity.

Of the eight, three are said to be historical personages—Zhongli Quan, Zhang Guolao and Lü Dongbin. The others—Tieguai Li, Han Xiangzi, Cao Guojiu, Lan Caihe and He Xiangu—are mentioned in fables.

The Eight Immortals have been regarded by the Chinese with a special adoration because they signify happiness. As a result of this tradition, the number 'eight' has been favoured by the Chinese as representing luck or good fortune.

Like other human beings on earth, the Chinese regard happiness as one of the most important qualities in life. The stories about the lives of the Eight Immortals show that it is possible for ordinary mortals to attain immortality and lasting happiness through selfless actions and good deeds.

The legend of the Eight Immortals as a group is not older than the time of the Yuan dynasty (AD 1271-1368) although individual members had been previously celebrated as immortals in Taoist tales as early as the Tang dynasty (AD 618-907).

Most people see the Eight Immortals simply as the subject of charming stories though they actually play a more significant role. This is in relationship to the Bagua, or Eight Trigrams, of the Yijing (also known as the I Ching in English), the most popular classic of traditional China.

The Eight Trigrams are a series of three lines, which combine all possible variations of either a broken line or a full line. They form one of the most important sets of symbols in Chinese divination.

Each of the Eight Immortals is associated with a certain direction of the Eight Trigrams. In certain cases this is based upon their nature. He Xiangu, a woman, represents yin, the female principle. She is associated with the south-west and the three broken lines of the trigram which represents yin is placed there. Because of his hot temper, Tieguai Li is situated in the south while the calmer and the eldest of the Eight, Zhang Guolao, is in the north.

Zhang Guolao
張果老

Lan Caihe
藍采和

Cao Guojiu
曹國舅

Lü Dongbin
呂洞賓

Zhongli Quan
鍾離權

Kan
坎

Gen
艮

Qian
乾

Dui
兌

Zhen
震

Kun
坤

Xun
巽

He Xiangu
何仙姑

Li
离

Han Xiangzi
韓湘子

Tieguai Li
鐵拐李

Zhongli Quan, whose fan stirs the seas, is in the east where the sea meets China. Lü Dongbin, subjugator of the forces of evil and the unknown, is on the west, traditionally the dwelling place of the mysterious and magical due to the vastness of the deserts and mountain ranges which lie in that direction.

Han Xiangzi defends the south-east while the last two, Lan Caihe and Cao Guojiu, guard the north-west and north-east respectively.

The Eight Immortals and their directions along the Eight Trigrams are invoked in one of the most powerful forms of magic in folk Taoism. This is the Bazhen Tu, the Battle Chart of the Eight Trigrams, used to counter the work of practitioners of black magic.

Traditional China is said to embrace the San Jiao, or Three Religions, of Taoism, Confucianism and Buddhism. Most ordinary Chinese felt closest to folk Taoism as Confucianism appealed to the educated while Buddhism had been regarded as a foreign religion since its advent in China.

Literacy was a privilege of a few as the vast majority of the people were unlettered. Thus not many people were familiar with Confucian or Buddhist teachings. Folk Taoism had the greatest appeal to these people because its teachings were often in the form of fables which could be transmitted widely by story-tellers.

It comes as no surprise, therefore, that the Eight Immortals are manifested in the form of stories rather than philosophical works.

Stories about the Eight Immortals appeared at a time when Buddhism was making inroads into the Chinese world as great teachers were able to popularize it among the masses by simplifying Buddhist teachings. Followers of Taoism, China's native philosophy, wanted to maintain its place in Chinese thought and one means of doing so was to make it more accessible to the masses.

Stories about the Eight Immortals helped the Chinese to easily assimilate Taoist teachings and the tradition has continued to this day.

Koh Kok Kiang

Contents

Tieguai Li
鐵拐李

Tieguai Li is always depicted with his iron crutch and gourd which contains magic medicines. His original name was Li Xuan. His popularity seems to rest on his irascible and unpredictable character. Tieguai Li is the patron saint of druggists and exorcists.

Reincarnation After Repentance

Tieguai Li's original name is said to be Li Xuan and he lived during the Sui Dynasty.

When he was young, his family was very poor. But he was a very filial son.

One year there was a severe drought and the harvest failed.

His father killed himself in despair.

His mother wept so much that she went blind.

Tieguai Li felt helpless.

He decided to go begging for food.

One day he noticed that someone had left a basket of carrots outside the house.

He decided to help himself to some of them.

Luckily for him his act went unnoticed.

Yippee! We are going to have carrots for dinner tonight.

My son, who is the kind soul who gave us so much to eat?

Soon it became a habit for him to steal.

3

It is so much easier to steal things than to beg for them.

Since then he had become habitually light-fingered.

Eventually he was caught red-handed.

People began to look at him with a jaundiced eye.

Every family would shut the door whenever he approached.

One night ...

He sneaked into someone's house.

4

6

If you are truly repentant, then return the wok at once.

Thank you for enlightening me!

That man saw that Tieguai Li was repentant.

Dawn was breaking …

Tieguai Li was worried that he would be apprehended when he returned the wok.

Please think of a way to help me.

Just go ahead and return it. When you have done so, come and see me. I intend to help you in some other way.

He raised his whisk and suddenly the sky turned dark again.

8

After those remarks, the man (a Taoist) disappeared.

The sky turned bright again.

Since then Tieguai Li had always been carrying the gourd with him everywhere to dispense medicine to cure sick people.

Eventually he went to live in a cave to practise the Tao.

One day, Laozi and Master Wan Qiu visited him and revealed to him the highest Taoist teachings.

On the sixth day …

Lang Ling, your mother is seriously ill.

He was a filial son and was anxious to see his mother. He cremated Tieguai Li's body.

Not long after, Tieguai Li was back.

He could not find his body.

While he was wondering what to do, he spotted the corpse of a person who had just died.

Tieguai Li decided to enter the man's body.

Why am I old and ugly?

12

Moreover, he was lame.

Oh, he is too ugly. I had better not use his body.

The action of Tao is not dependent on appearances. I'll give you an iron crutch to help you move about.

With this crutch, you can go anywhere.

Since then Tieguai Li roamed everywhere to help the sick and became one of the Eight Immortals.

Zhongli Quan
鐘離權

His family name was said to be Zhongli and he lived during the Han dynasty. Hence he is also known as Han Zhongli. He was said to have been a military officer. He is often shown bare-bellied and carrying a feathery fan which controls the seas.

Zhongli Quan Attains Immortality After Suffering Great Hardship

Zhongli Quan was from Yantai in Shandong Province and his father was a marquis. It was said that at the time of his birth a supernatural being entered the confinement room.

At the moment of his birth, the room was illuminated by a bright light which shone like raging fire.

Wah! Wah!

He was born with a round head and high forehead.

18

Ouch!

These rascals deserve to be taught a lesson.

When he grew up, he became a general.

One day, he embarked on a military expedition to fight Tufan forces in what is now Tibet.

He was in charge of the troops.

As they were nearing the Tufan territory …

Because of the superior size of the Tufan army and Zhongli Quan's lack of battlefield experience, the expedition ended in defeat.

Zhongli Quan fled amidst the tumult.

He rode into a valley.

He then realized that he had lost his way.

Feeling exhausted, he was not inclined to find a way out immediately.

Suddenly a monk appeared in front of him.

Please follow me.

The monk led him to a manor.

This is where Master Donghua practised the Toa. You may as well take a rest here.

Zhongli Quan dared not disturb the people there and roamed about by himself.

That person is Zhongli Quan.

Aren't you General Zhongli Quan? Why not come into the house?

Zhongli Quan was greatly surprised and knew that the old man was no ordinary person. Having just got out of danger, he was in no mood to leave and dropped to his knees.

He implored the old man to teach him the Tao.

Hmmm ...

The old man taught him the arts of immortality.

He learned about the Tao for a long time.

When he looked back after bidding the old man farewell, the manor had vanished into thin air.

Later, he met the Immortal Huayang and learned an even more profound way of Taoism.

From then on he wandered all over the country and finally realized the Tao on Si Hao Peak and became an immortal.

Zhang Guolao
張果老

He is said to have lived in the 7th or 8th century AD and is often pictured riding his donkey backwards. His symbol is the fish drum which consists of a bamboo tube with smaller tubes emerging at the top. He is venerated as one who brings male offspring.

He Shouwu And Guolao Temple

Zhang Guolao was born in a poor family and he made his living carrying goods on his donkey.

One afternoon, he led his donkey to a dilapidated temple hoping to get some rest.

Zhang Guolao had only a little food with him.

Shall I keep this piece for my dinner?

Just as he was leaving ...

Wow! Wonderful smell!

A delicious aroma wafted from the temple.

He decided to trace the source of the aroma.

He peered through the doorway of the temple.

There was no one in the temple but there was a wok with something being cooked in it.

The aroma came from the stew of a meat-like herb being cooked in the wok.

Strange! How come the cook did not eat the food at home but left it here at the temple?

The aroma is irresistible!

Zhang Guolao went out to take a look but did not see anybody.

He decided to use twigs to improvise as chopsticks.

He thoroughly relished the food.

Actually, there was a story behind the wok of food.

Not far from the temple was an eccentric teacher.

He sought immortality through physical practices.

Teacher, in that desolate spot is a bare-bottomed child who wanted to play with me.

One day, a student told him …

It must be the shouwu herb spirit.

Whoever eats it will become an immortal.

Hence he thought of a way of tracing the source of the herb using a red thread and a needle.

He took hold of one end of the thread and asked his student to attach the needle holding the other end to the bare-bottomed child.

The following day, the boy appeared again to play and the student acted as he was told.

He followed the thread to find out where the shouwu spirit dwelled.

At the back of the temple, he spotted the shouwu plant.

He started digging.

It turned out to be a shouwu of good size.

He cooked the herb in the temple only to realize that he lacked eating utensils.

Just as he was on his way home to get eating utensils, he ran into an old friend.

Teacher, how about writing a pair of couplets for me?

After he had finished writing the couplets, his friend invited him to tea.

Meanwhile, back at the temple ...

Zhang Guolao could not finish all the food and noticed that his donkey appeared hungry.

He gave the remainder to the donkey.

He splashed what was left of the soup on a wall.

As he was leading his donkey away, he saw the highly agitated teacher approaching.

Oh no! The owner is here!

Time to flee!

Zhang Guolao and the donkey rose into the air.

The abandoned chopsticks grew into a pair of huge trees and became known as Guolao trees.

The wall of the temple on which the stew was splashed became as solid as iron and could not be toppled.

After the story of how Zhang Guolao became an immortal circulated among the people, the temple came to be known as Guolao Temple.

Lü Dongbin
呂洞賓

Lü Dongbin is the most popular of the Eight Immortals. He is seen as a healer of the poor and a slayer of evil spirits. His symbols are a Devil Slayer sword and a bushy fly whisk which enables him to fly at will. Lü Dongbin is the patron saint of barbers.

Lü Dongbin Attains Immortality Through Perseverance

Lü Dongbin was born in the Tang Dynasty. His father and grandfather were court officials. When his mother was pregnant, an exotic fragrance filled the room and there was heavenly music.

A white crane descended from the sky.

Shortly, Lü Dongbin was born.

It flew into the room and vanished into his mother's womb.

Lü Dongbin had been exceptionally clever since young.

He could easily memorise and recite the Confucian classics.

When he was at Mount Lushan, he met the Fire Dragon Immortal who taught him advanced swordplay.

He went to Chang'an, the capital, twice to sit for the imperial examinations.

However, he was unsuccessful both times. He was then 42 years old.

One day, he was having a drink at an inn.

Zhongli Quan come.

Yes, please.

May I sit here?

You look downcast. Is something bothering you?

It was not easy for Lü Dongbin to find a person who understood him, so he told Zhongli Quan about all the things that turned out against his wishes.

They drank and chatted and before long Lü Dongbin fell into a drunken stupor.

Zhongli Quan took Lü Dongbin to rest at his hut.

As Lü Dongbin was resting, Zhongli Quan went to cook millet.

Lü Dongbin dreamt that he became the top scholar and rose steadily in his official career. He also enjoyed a blissful family life.

Eventually he became the prime minister and held the post for many years.

One day, he offended the new emperor who feared his influence and his entire family was executed. He was sent into exile and was in desperate straits.

Lü Dongbin awoke with a start and was gripped by fear.

You have finished your dream before the millet is cooked.

The greatest happiness in life is to be associated with the spirit, and the greatest misery is to know too much and yet be unable to be detached.

How do you know I was dreaming?

You must be an immortal. Please accept me as your disciple.

Sure, but there are conditions.

One day, Lü Dongbin's entire family died. He felt no sadness. All he did was to make the funeral arrangements.

Having passed this test, his family rose from the dead.

Another day, after he had agreed on a price with a merchant, the man went back on his word.

He did not argue and paid the price.

On another occasion, he met a beggar and gave him some valuables. Not only was the beggar ungrateful, he also berated Lü Dongbin, who apologized for offending him.

45

He came across a tiger about to attack a flock of sheep and shielded them with his body.

At the sight of the imposing figure, the tiger turned around and fled.

Once while he was tilling the field …

He found some gold coins.

He didn't even touch a single one and covered them up.

He bought a bronze vessel and when he reached home and realized that it was actually made of gold, he returned it to the seller.

Whoever eats it is sure to die, but he will be able to learn the Tao in his next life.

A Taoist was selling "sure-to-die" pills and no one dared to buy them.

However, no harm befell him.

It was the onset of spring and Lü Dongbin was crossing the swollen stream with others.

Suddenly the current became very strong.

All the people were crossing warily.

Others became frightened but Lü Dongbin did not harbour any thoughts of life and death.

He remained composed.

Lü Dongbin went to live alone in a mountain hut.

One day a beautiful girl appeared.

She begged to go to bed with him.

Lü Dongbin felt no desire.

Once while he was alone at home ...

48

Many evil spirits appeared and wanted to attack him. He was completely unafraid.

Another night there appeared a ghastly figure who claimed that he was killed by Lü Dongbin in a previous life and wanted the blood debt to be repaid.

A killer deserves to be killed. This is logical and just.

Stop!

Suddenly there was a shout and all the apparitions disappeared.

Zhongli Quan appeared.

Lü Dongbin, you have passed my tests.

Zhongli Quan taught him to ride the clouds. Lü Dongbin practised Taoism for a long time and eventually became an immortal.

49

Cao Guojiu
曹國舅

According to one legend, he was the brother of Empress Cao, mother of Emperor Ying Zong of the Song dynasty. He is shown wearing official robes and a court head-dress. In his hands are an imperial tablet and a pair of castanets.

Cao Guojiu Becomes An Immortal By Reformation

Cao Guojiu's original name was Cao Yi. Cao Yi was the emperor's uncle and thus came to be known as Guojiu (emperor's uncle).

Cao Guojiu and his two brothers were bullies.

They liked to hunt for pleasure.

I don't feel well.

Quick! Finish them off and seize the valuables.

Cao Guojiu had added a drug to the drink to knock them out.

Oh!

Suddenly a whirlwind descended.

When the wind died down, the drugged victims and the valuables were nowhere to be seen.

What's going on?

There must be spirits around!

That night.

Cao Guojiu had a frightful dream.

55

Cao Guojiu,
pay with
your life!

Hold
it!

When the Taoist man appeared, all the ghosts disappeared. The Taoist man told him: "Repent before it is too late."

From then onwards, Cao Guojiu decided to make up for his past wrongdoings.

Whenever there was a famine, he would provide free food.

He also provided medical help by opening an apothecary. The poor did not have to pay for treatment.

Doctor, what's wrong with him?

He has a fever. These pills will cure him.

Cao Guojiu's two brothers strongly opposed what he was doing.

Our fortune will soon be gone.

He also set up a charitable home to house those who were unable to fend for themselves.

One morning ...

Your Lordship, this is terrible!

All the residents in the charitable home had been poisoned and Cao Guojiu was very sad over their deaths.

He was quick in getting to the bottom of the matter. His two brothers were responsible and he had them arrested and sent for execution.

Cao Guojiu travelled to learn the Tao. When Lü Dongbin saw that he had repented and was sincere, he helped him become an immortal.

Han Xiangzi
韓湘子

He is said to be a nephew of the famous Tang dynasty scholar Han Yu. His emblem is the flute. A lover of solitude, he represents the ideal of a contented person dwelling in natural places. He did not know the value of money and, if given any, used to scatter it on the ground. Han Xiangzi is the patron saint of musicians.

The Exquisite Sound Of Flute Moves Heaven

Han Xiangzi's parents died when he was young and so
he went to live with his uncle.

At the age of eight he could compose poetry and at the age of sixteen
he had passed the second highest level of the imperial examinations.

Some time later, Han Yu offended the emperor and was exiled.

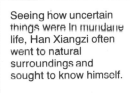

He was exiled to Chaozhou, a poor and desolate place.

Overnight, Han Yu's residence became deserted and relatives and friends shunned the house.

Human emotions are fickle. What does high and low mean anyway?

Seeing how uncertain things were in mundane life, Han Xiangzi often went to natural surroundings and sought to know himself.

Han Xiangzi gave up reading Confucian literature such as the Four Books and Five Classics.

He spent his time playing a bamboo flute.

He also spent his time drinking tea or wine with talented people.

One day, Han Xiangzi went to the Lijiang River and saw an old man playing a flute.

The sound of the flute was refined and exquisite.

Marvellous! It's a wonder to hear something like this in the human world.

In a moment of exuberance, Han Xiangzi also played a tune with his flute.

Master Han, do you want to compete with me? Let's see who can attract the divine flute.

Based on what you said, I would like to give it a try.

Han Xiangzi began playing tunes he was familiar with on his flute.

This won't do. What you are playing are the same old tunes. How can it move the divine flute?

What should I do then?

You should travel to look for a really good teacher first.

Han Xiangzi left his uncle's mansion and travelled from place to place.

Somebody was playing a tune on a flute.

What a marvellous sound!

He went to trace the source of the music.

He saw a girl who was so absorbed in playing the flute that she did not notice him.

So she's the musician.

Lin Ying, you resemble my childhood playmate.

Her name was Xiaomei. Twenty years have passed.

I wonder how she is now.

Lin Ying, when I am with you, I have indescribable sweet feeling. I ...

Han Xiangzi had spoken what was in his heart.

I'm very sorry that I cannot accept your love. You see, I already have a partner.

No more was said that night.

Dawn broke.

Indeed Lin Ying had a fiance who seemed to have returned from a trip.

Han Xiangzi, that's the end of the matter.

Han Xiangzi wrote a poem to describe his feelings.

Han Xiangzi went to the Lijiang River and played the flute to express his sorrow.

This tune is very touching. I've never heard anything so moving.

The divine flute is appearing!

From the water appeared a lustrous jade flute.

You are now freed of worldly cares.

He practised the Tao and made progress.

Before long, with the help of the flute, Han Xiangzi attained immortality.

Lan Caihe
藍朶和

Lan Caihe is the strangest of the eight, being at times male and at times female. He is often shown carrying a basket of flowers. He represents the odd figure who does not fit into social categories. Lan Caihe is the patron saint of florists.

Lan Caihe Jumps On The Divine Raft

Lan Caihe was originally a barefoot deity in heaven. However, he offended the Celestial Lord and was banished to earth.

It's a male child.

Waa!

Lan Caihe was born in the family of official Lan who was delighted to have a male child at his advanced age.

When he was one year old, Lan Caihe became fond of books and lost interest in toys.

When he was three, his mother died of a serious illness.

His father remarried and had two more sons.

At a young age Lan Caihe could recite poetry and he was fascinated by *Dao De Jing*.

When he was eight, his father died.

Father!

His stepmother began to show her fierce nature.

She did not give him enough food or clothing.

Eventually she drove him out of the house.

In the day time he recited stories and poems to make a living.

At night he slept in a rundown temple.

Lan Caihe was hardworking and good-natured. The people were willing to help him.

One day, he saw a lame man revive a person who had died.

Immortal, I, Lan Caihe implore you to accept me as your disciple.

Immortal, accept us as your disciples as well.

You want to become an immortal like me? No problem. Tomorrow, just go to the building overlooking the river. The divine raft will come.

78

The bamboo leaf grew in size and lifted Lan Caihe into the sky.

Although Lan Caihe was young, he became one of the Eight Immortals.

He Xiangu
何仙姑

The only woman in the group, she is often shown holding a lotus bloom, the flower of open-heartedness, which reflects her nature. She is portrayed as an exceptionally beautiful maiden.

The Lotus Flower And He Xiangu

He Xiangu was a native of Niujiao county by the Huai River.

Her parents died when she was young and she went to work for an old woman when she grew up.

The old woman was lazy and made He Xiangu do all the chores.

He Xiangu had to work non-stop from dawn to midnight every day.

He Xiangu was kind-hearted by nature and would give food to the poor.

The old woman often beat her.

One day ...

I'm going out. You must grind the beans.

He Xiangu worked all alone. She poured the liquid made from the beans into a big wok.

At this time, seven people came to the door.

Have pity on us!

We have not eaten for three days.

Who are you all?

They had a gaunt look and wore ragged clothes.

Please!

Miss, help us!

He Xiangu was moved by their distress. She quickly gave a ladleful of soya milk to Tieguai Li.

The six others surged forward and He Xiangu was put in a difficult position as she knew that if the old woman returned, she would be punished for giving food away.

Please help us!

Am I not a poor person like them? I ought to help them.

You are all also poor people. I will give you soya milk even if I get beaten for doing so.

In no time they finished drinking the soya milk.

After giving their thanks to her, the seven men left.

Soon the old woman returned.

She noticed that a lot of soya beans were used but there was very little bean curd produced.

How come there's so little of it?

He Xiangu had no choice but to tell her what happened.

You go look for the seven men and bring them here. Otherwise I will break your legs.

He Xiangu held back her tears and went to look for the seven men.

Soon she came upon them.

She told them what happened after they had left the house.

That's too much! We will go back with you.

The old woman was standing at the door.

88

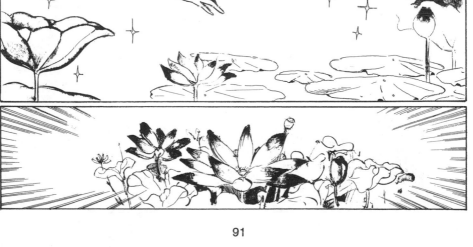

The solitary lotus flower in the pond turned into numerous plants which covered the pond.

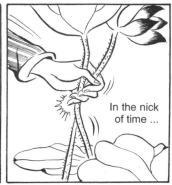

In the nick of time ...

92

He Xiangu rose into the air like an immortal.

The old woman could not catch up with her.

He Xiangu, thank you for the soya milk.

So you are the immortals!

Just now you drank the soya milk we vomited. It can neutralize poisons and make you an immortal.

He Xiangu became an immortal because of her kind nature. She is also the only female among the Eight Immortals. She has a refined and gentle look and is often seen holding a lotus bloom which she uses to cure the sick.

The Eight Immortals Cross the Sea
八仙過海

In a certain year, the Eight Immortals were on their way home after attending the Peach of Immortality Gathering hosted by the Queen Mother on the third day of the third lunar month.

The Immortals were inebriated after attending the gathering.

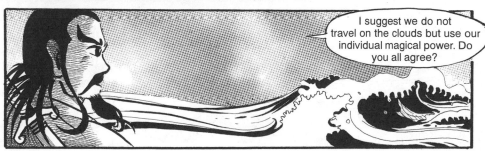

Agreed!

Lü Dongbin hurled his sword across the sea.

The sword turned into a small boat which moved with the wind.

Tieguai Li turned his iron crutch into a piece of wood.

Han Xiangzi turned his flower basket into a boat. He Xiangu stood on a giant lotus.

Lan Caihe turned his jade board into a canoe while Cao Guojiu transformed his bamboo container into a raft.

Zhongli Quan stood on a huge banana leaf whereas Zhang Guolao rode on his paper donkey.

The Eight Immortals came to the palace of the Dragon King.

What's that?

I'm going to search for He Xiangu.

Lü Dongbin arrived at the palace but the sea creatures blocked his way.

They were no match for Lü Dongbin.

Dragon Crown Prince, release He Xiangu quickly!

Lü Dongbin arrived at the Crown Prince's residence.

What if I do not release her?

The Crown Prince and Lü Dongbin engaged in a fierce combat.

Lü Dongbin used his gourd to heat up the sea until it was boiling hot.

Dragon King's Palace

Lü Dongbin, how dare you charge into my palace. Do you know this is a heavenly offence?

Dragon King, do you know that your supposedly good son has taken He Xiangu by force?

110

112

The fierce battle shook heaven and earth.

116

Ah! My troops are losing the fight. If this goes on, even the palace will be in danger of destruction.

I have a plan.

Zhang Guolao's paper donkey cleared a path for the Immortals to leave the darkened palace.

A giant octopus had squirted a black liquid into the palace.

Let me deal with it.

Let's forget it. Otherwise when will such vengence end?

The Immortals decided to let the matter rest and return to the surface.

Eventually, the Immortals crossed the Eastern Sea in a happy mood.

CHINESE CLASSICS

THE BIRTH OF THE MONKEY KING

Illustrated by Chang Boon Kiat.
150x210mm, 144 pages,
ISBN 981-229-127-X.

The irreverent Sun Wukong is the best-loved of the character in the popular Chinese literary classic, *Journey to the West*. *The Birth of the Monkey King* relates how he came into existence in the Mountain of Flowers and Fruit, and his many adventures before entering the service of Xuanzang. Be entertained by Monkey's mischief and cleverness as he fights demons and monsters from underwater and the celestial realm.

ADVENTURES OF THE MONKEY KING

Illustrated by Chang Boon Kiat.
150x210mm, 160 pages,
ISBN 978-981-229-464-7

This is the sequel to *The Birth of the Monkey King*. Featuring the same lovable illustrations, rib-tickling twists and a galloping plot, *Adventures of the Monkey King* promises to leave you breathless with exhilaration as the rebellious Sun Wukong and his fellow travellers run headlong into all sorts of adversities as they head west to gather scriptures as instructed by the Tang emperor.

Jokes & Humour

FUN WITH SPORTS; MORE FUN WITH SPORTS
128pp, comics, ISBN 981-229-406-6,
Welcome to the amusing world of sports! Forget the grime, the determination and all that hard work – this book isn't about the blood, sweat and tears you hear so often about. We're taking a look at the FUNNY side of sports.

SOCCER JOY; MORE SOCCER JOY
112pp, comics, ISBN 981-3029-10-2, 981-229-270-9.
Nunk's constructive humour in *Soccer Joy* allows us to see the lighter side of this wonderful sport. *Soccer Joy*, better known as *Sepakbolaria* in the original Indonesian edition is very popular with the soccer fans there. Whether you are a player or a spectator, you will enjoy Soccer Joy tremendously.

FUNNY JOKES; MORE FUNNY JOKES
128pp, ISBN 981-229-186-5, 981-229-214-4.
Treat yourself to the latest jokes, riddles and comic tales from Asia. The funny stuff here is hilarious, zany yet thought-provoking. So dive in for a whacky time!

WITTY TALES FROM ASIA; WHACKY JOKES
120-128pp, ISBN 981-229-223-3, 981-229-278-0.
Witty Tales From Asia is chock-a-block with whacky tales and jokes gathered from various parts of Asia. The memorable stories are sure to leave you in stitches! Follow Vazir Birbal, a courtier of King Akbar, in *Whacky Jokes* as he solves countless knotty problems with his quick wit and tongue-in-cheek humour.

FUN WITH RIDDLES; RIDDLES FOR SMART KIDS
128pp, ISBN 981-229-355-8, 981-229-278-0;
981-229-438-4
Test yourself against the countless riddles, from witty puns to mind-boggling brain-teasers and cracked wise proverbs. And once you are successfully through, you will be charged to test your family and pals. Meet the challenge head-on!

LOVE STORIES FROM ANCIENT CHINA

This book features 16 great love stories, including Cowherd and Weaver Girl, Liang Shanbo and Zhu Yingtai, Meng Jiang Nü as well as Madam White Snake and Xu Mian. You will also enjoy romantic verses penned by renowned Chinese poets. Not only will the adorable characters amuse and steal your heart, their stories will also move you to tears. Be inspired by the power of everlasting love.

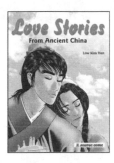

THE THREE KINGDOMS

This compact edition brings you the highlights of this magnificent historical novel, including well-known episodes such as "oath of brotherhood at the Peach Garden", Liu Bei's thre visits to Zhuge Liang's cottage and the Battle of Red Cliff. It will lead you through the ups and downs of the heroes of the ancient times, at times admiring their courage, and at other times lamenting their fate.

ORIGINS OF CHINESE NAMES

Find out the origins of 100 Chinese family names, and understand how names are chosen. It may fascinate you to know that Chinese family names have a history of five or six thousand years, whilst given names are not chosen randomly but reflect the customs and beliefs of the times.

TOP CRIME MYSTERIES

More than 20 baffling crimes, all solved through the knowledge and reasoning skills of the detectives and experts handling each case. Put on your thinking caps and find out more about how crimes are solved!

八仙过海

绘画 ：陈国胜

翻译 ：许国强

亚太图书有限公司出版